Big Barry Baker's parcel

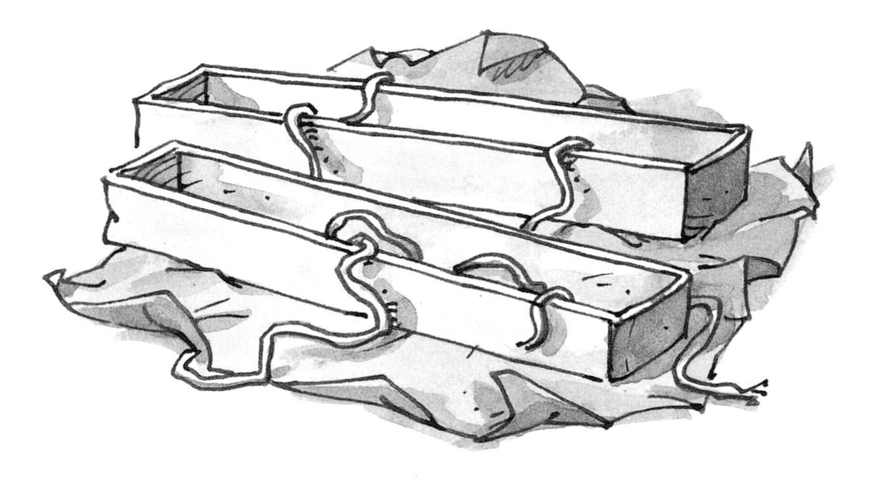

Written by Gill and Paul Hamlyn
Illustrated by Philippe Dupasquier

Chapter 1

Big Barry Baker and his three friends, Josie, Liz and Roy, were on their way to school. When they got to the top of the road they looked back and saw a red van stopping outside Big Barry Baker's house. A postman got out. He was carrying a parcel.

'Look, Barry,' they said. 'He's going to your house.'

They watched the postman giving the parcel to Big Barry Baker's mum.

'What do you think it is?' asked Josie.

'Let's go and see,' said Barry.

The four friends ran back to Big Barry Baker's house. Barry's mum smiled at them and said, 'It's a parcel from Grandad.'

Big Barry Baker looked at the parcel.

'It's for me!' he shouted.

‘Please can I open it now?’ he asked.

‘No,’ said his mum. ‘You’ll be late for school. You can open it tonight.’

Big Barry Baker wasn’t happy.

He wanted to open the parcel quickly, but he did as he was told and gave it back to his mum.

The four friends set off for school again, but they couldn't stop talking about the parcel.

'The parcel is very long,' said Barry. 'What do you think it is?'

‘I think it’s a stick of rock,’ said Josie.

‘I think it’s a telescope,’ said Liz.

‘I think it’s a big banana,’ said Roy.

They all laughed.

All day Big Barry Baker and his friends talked about the parcel. They talked about it at play time, they talked about it in the classroom, and they talked about it at lunch time. At last it was time to go home.

'Come on,' said Barry. 'Let's find out what's in the parcel.'

They all ran to Barry's house as fast as they could.

‘Mum, where’s the parcel from Grandad?’ asked Barry as he pushed open the door. ‘Here it is,’ she said with a smile. Josie, Liz and Roy watched as Barry opened the long box.

He pulled out a cricket bat with a long black handle, and a red ball.

'Wow!' said Barry.

Chapter 2

The next day Big Barry Baker took his new cricket bat and ball to school. All the children wanted a look.

'Let's play cricket,' Barry shouted. 'Watch me hit the ball.'

He gave the ball to Liz. 'You can be the bowler.'

Liz had watched cricket on the television so she knew what to do. She walked away from Big Barry Baker. She stopped and turned, then she ran across the playground and bowled the ball.

But Big Barry Baker missed.

So Liz bowled the ball again but not so fast.

Big Barry Baker missed again.

All the children laughed.

'Big Barry Baker can't hit the ball,' they called out.

Barry was cross.

'I don't like cricket,' he said. 'I don't want to play.'

'You can't be good at everything first time,' said Liz. 'You need to keep trying.'

'I know,' said Roy. 'Let's go to the park after school. We can all have another go there.'

Chapter 3

After school Big Barry Baker, Josie, Liz and Roy went to the park. Big Barry Baker tried to bat but he could not hit the ball.

'Why don't you have a go at bowling?' said Josie. 'I'll bat now.'

So Big Barry Baker had a go at bowling. He bowled the ball as hard as he could and the ball went so fast that Josie didn't even see it.

Big Barry Baker had another go.
Josie missed the ball again.
Big Barry Baker was a good bowler.

Next it was Liz's turn to bat and Roy's turn to be the bowler.

Liz hit the ball in the air.

'Catch it!' shouted Roy.

Big Barry Baker jumped up for the ball.

'Out!' he shouted, and he opened up his hands to show everyone the ball.

Big Barry Baker was good at catching too!

Chapter 4

The next day Big Barry Baker took
his bat and ball to school again.
'Who wants to play cricket?'
he shouted out.
All the children wanted to play, so
they began to pick sides.

‘We don’t want Big Barry Baker on our side,’ said the other children. ‘He’s no good at cricket.’

Josie, Liz and Roy looked at one another and smiled.

‘Come with us, Big Barry Baker,’ they said. ‘We want you on our side.’

So the children started to play. Big Barry Baker was the first to bat. He tried and tried but he could not hit the ball. All the other children laughed.

But soon it was Big Barry Baker's turn to be the bowler. Every time he bowled the ball it went so fast that the children could not hit it. Only one boy hit the ball. Big Barry Baker jumped up.

'Out!' he shouted.

B

'We won, we won!' said Josie, Liz and Roy. 'All thanks to Big Barry Baker!'

Big Barry Baker smiled. He looked down at his cricket bat and ball.

'Thanks, Grandad,' he said. 'Maybe one day you'll come and show me how to bat. Then I'll be a real cricketer!'